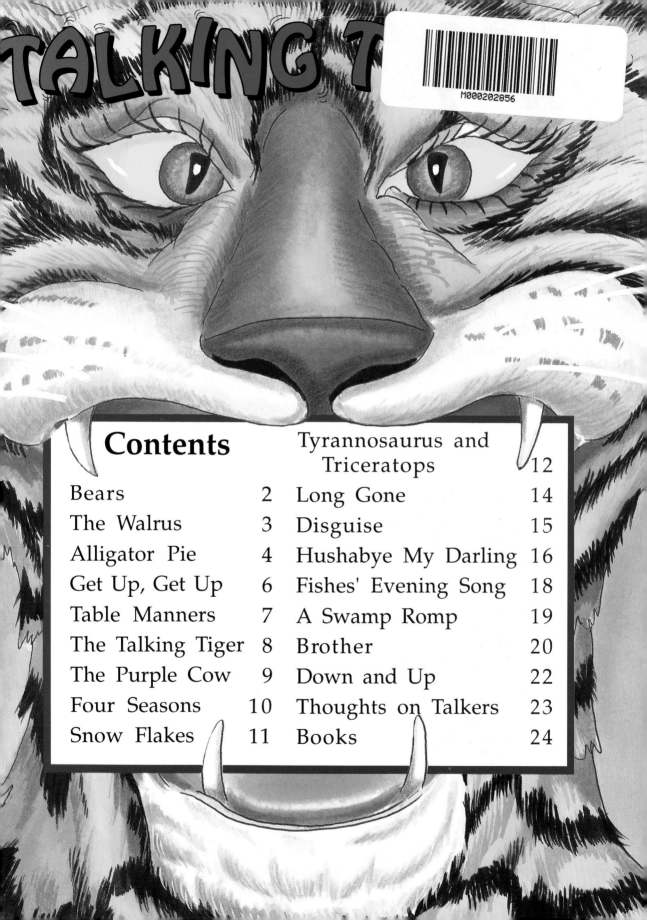

TALKING T

Contents

Bears

Bears, bears, bears, bears, bears
On the stairs
Under chairs
Washing hairs
Giving stares
Collecting fares
Stepping in squares
Millionaires
Everywheres
Bears, bears, bears, bears, bears.

Ruth Krauss

The Walrus

The widdly, waddly walrus
has flippery, floppery feet.
He dives in the ocean for dinner
and stands on his noggin to eat.

The wrinkly, crinkly walrus
swims with a debonair splash.
His elegant tusks are of ivory
and he wears a fine walrus moustache.

Jack Prelutsky

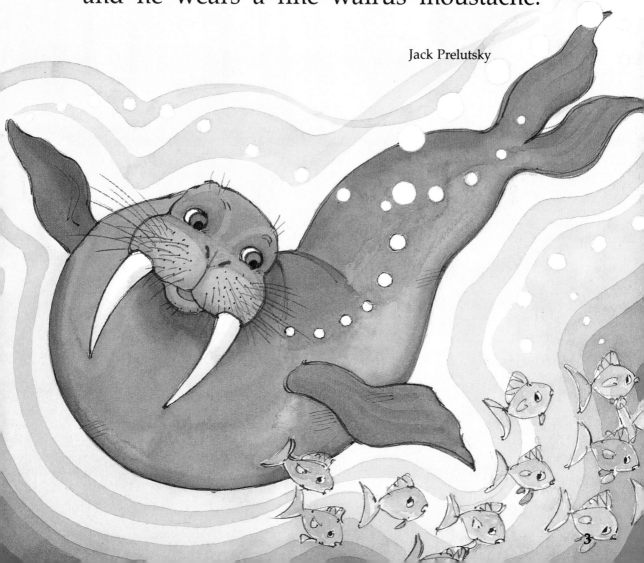

Alligator Pie

Alligator pie, alligator pie,
  If I don't get some
I think I'm gonna die.
  Give away the green grass,
Give away the sky,
  But don't give away my alligator pie.

Alligator stew, alligator stew,
  If I don't get some
I don't know what I'll do.
  Give away my furry hat,
Give away my shoe,
  But don't give away my alligator stew.

Alligator soup, alligator soup,
  If I don't get some
I think I'm gonna droop.
  Give away my hockey-stick,
Give away my hoop,
  But don't give away my alligator soup.

Dennis Lee

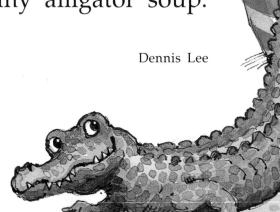

4

Get Up, Get Up

Get up, get up, you lazy heads
Get up you lazy bunch,
We need those sheets for table-cloths,
It's nearly time for lunch!

Anonymous

Table Manners

The Goops they lick their fingers,
  And the Goops they lick their knives;
They spill their broth on the table-cloth —
  Oh, they live untidy lives!

The Goops they talk while eating,
  And loud and fast they chew,
So that is why I'm glad that I
  Am not a Goop — are you?

Gelett Burgess

The Talking Tiger

If a tiger
Walks beside you
And he whispers:
"Where are you going?"
Do not answer,
Just keep walking
Just keep walking, walking, walking.
And if he continues talking
You keep walking.

Arnold Spilka

The Purple Cow

I never saw a purple cow,
I never hope to see one;
But I can tell you, anyhow,
I'd rather see than be one.

Gelett Burgess

Four Seasons

Spring is showery, flowery, bowery.
Summer: hoppy, choppy, poppy.
Autumn: wheezy, sneezy, freezy.
Winter: slippy, drippy, nippy.

Anonymous

Snow Flakes

Feathery flakes of snow come down,
Swirling, twirling, drifting,
Until they cover all the town,
Swirling, twirling, drifting,
People hurry to and fro,
Riding, sliding, skipping,
Through the silvery powdered snow,
Riding, sliding, skipping,
Motor cars are going home,
Shifting, swerving, dripping,
Through the swirling snowy foam,
Shifting, swerving, dripping.

Louise Abney

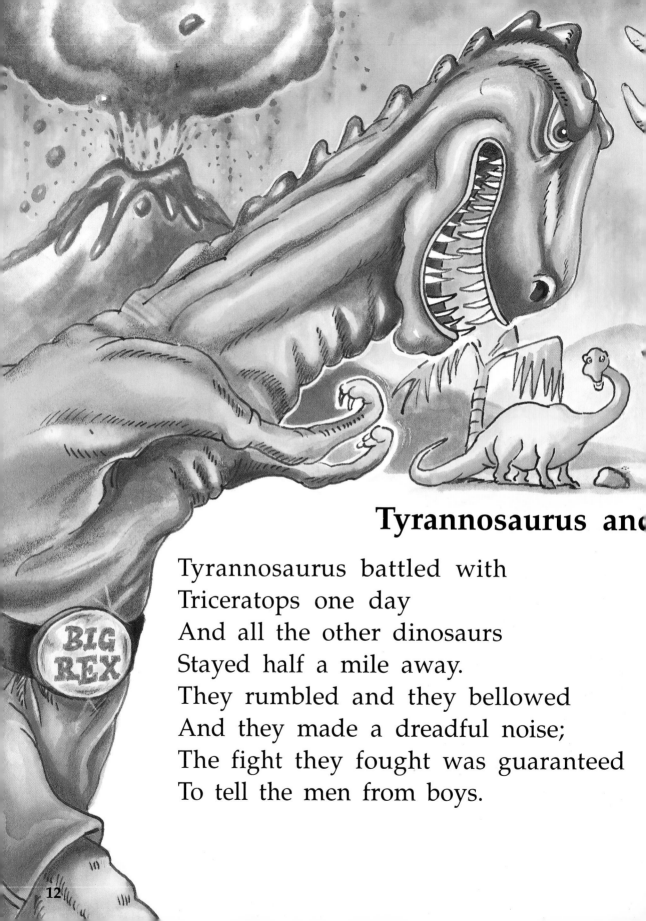

Tyrannosaurus and

Tyrannosaurus battled with
Triceratops one day
And all the other dinosaurs
Stayed half a mile away.
They rumbled and they bellowed
And they made a dreadful noise;
The fight they fought was guaranteed
To tell the men from boys.

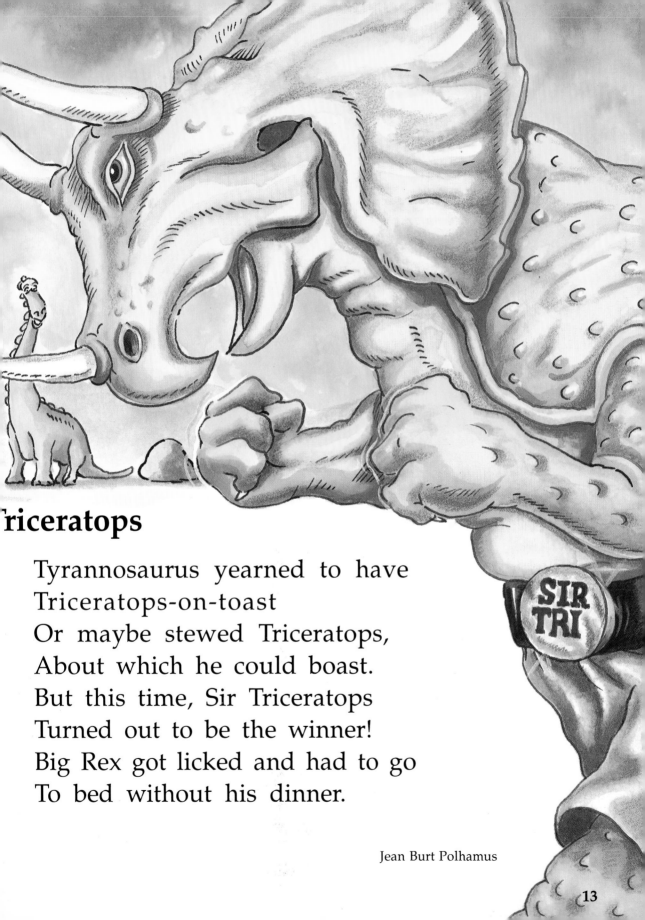

Triceratops

Tyrannosaurus yearned to have
Triceratops-on-toast
Or maybe stewed Triceratops,
About which he could boast.
But this time, Sir Triceratops
Turned out to be the winner!
Big Rex got licked and had to go
To bed without his dinner.

Jean Burt Polhamus

13

Long Gone

Don't waste your time in looking for
the long-extinct tyrannosaur,
because this ancient dinosaur
just can't be found here anymore.

This also goes for stegosaurus,
allosaurus, brontosaurus
and any other saur or saurus.
They all lived here long before us.

Jack Prelutsky

Disguise

There once was a lady called Maggie,
Whose dog was enormous and shaggy,
The front end of him
Looked vicious and grim —
But the back end was friendly and waggy.

Anonymous

Hushabye My Darling

Hushabye my darling
Don't you make a peep
Little creatures everywhere
Are settling down to sleep

Fishes in the millpond
Goslings in the barn
Kitten by the fireside
Baby in my arms

Listen to the raindrops
Singing you to sleep
Hushabye my darling
Don't you make a peep

Clyde Watson

Fishes' Evening Song

Flip flop,
Flip flap,
Slip slap,
Lip lap;
Water sounds,
Soothing sounds.
We fan our fins
As we lie
Resting here
Eye to eye.
Water falls
Drop by drop,
Plip plop,
Drip drop.
Plink plunk,
Splash splish
Fish fins fan,
Fish tails swish,
Swush, swash, swish.
This we wish . . .
Water cold,
Water clear,
Water smooth,
Just to soothe
Sleepy fish.

Dahlov Ipcar

A Swamp Romp

Clomp Thump
Swamp Lump
Plodding in the Ooze,
Belly Shiver
Jelly Quiver
Squelching in my shoes.

Clomp Thump
Romp Jump
Mulching all the Mud,
Boot Trudge
Foot Sludge
Thud! Thud! Thud!

Doug MacLeod

Brother

I had a little brother
And I brought him to my mother
And I said I want another
Little brother for a change.

But she said don't be a bother
So I took him to my father
And I said this little bother
Of a brother's very strange.

But he said one little brother
Is exactly like another
And every little brother
Misbehaves a bit he said.

So I took the little bother
From my mother and my father
And I put the little bother
Of a brother back to bed.

Mary Ann Hoberman

Down and Up

Max Fatchen

Words
are
nice
to
speak
and
read
and
some
are
very
long
indeed
and
if
you
are
the
reading
age
you'll
reach
the
bottom
of
this
page.

Now read across.

top.
very
the
reach
you
until
stop
never
and
along
read
so
play
to
out
come
us
like
words
for
way
different
a
quite
going
we're

We'd like to say

Thoughts on Talkers

Some people talk in a telephone,
And some people talk in a hall;
Some people talk in a whisper,
And some people talk in a drawl;
And some people talk-and-
               talk-and-
                  talk-and-
                     talk- and- talk
And never say anything at all.

Walter R. Brooks

Books

Books to the ceiling, books to the sky.
My piles of books are a mile high.
How I love them!
How I need them!
I'll have a long beard
by the time I read them.

Arnold Lobel